Aural Time!

Practice Tests for ABRSM and Other Exams

Grade 4

DAVID TURNBULL

CONTENTS

Bosworth

4.95

INTRODUCTION

Changes in some examination syllabuses which take effect from 1st January 1995 have made a revised edition of *Aural Time!* Book 4 necessary. Much of the material of the first edition has nevertheless been retained.

Teachers may like to use this booklet to supplement other aural training material. Like most musical skills, aural awareness needs regular practice, and aural training should be part of every lesson.

Many of the examples in this booklet will be found helpful by candidates who hope to offer music in the GCSE, as well as for those taking grade examinations.

As in other volumes in the series, many of the examples are taken from songs. It is hoped that thereby the interest of pupils may be stimulated in this great area of musical achievement.

Examples have often been adapted to make them more suitable for their present purpose. As far as possible, accompaniments have been kept simple, as not all good instrumental teachers are necessarily fluent pianists.

David Turnbull

August 1994

A Note about Musical Features

In many types of music examination pupils are asked about features of a piece of music played. These include **rhythm, melody, dynamics** (including gradations of dynamics like *crescendo* and *diminuendo*, **articulation** of notes, **tempo** (including changes to tempo), **tonality** (the choice of **keys**), **harmony**, the **texture** of the music, particularly homophony and counterpoint, and the general **form** of the piece being examined. Questions of this type appear in the ABRSM Grade 4 examination as well as in others, and teachers sometimes ask for further guidance.

The way the composer uses these features gives to a piece its **character**. For example, if a piece is slow in tempo, is written in a minor key, has articulation which is largely *legato* and has dynamics which are mostly *piano*, the character of the music is likely to be sad. If a piece of music is fast in tempo, in a major key, has articulation which is sometimes *staccato* and dynamics which are often *forte*, the character of the music is likely to seem bright and cheerful.

1

Test A. Memorising Melodies

GRADE 4

These melodies will be played twice. The keychord and the starting note will be played and named. The pulse will be tapped. Pupils may then **either** sing **or** play the melodies.

Sometimes, pupils find at first that they cannot remember all of a melody. Teachers may like to divide some melodies into phrases to help.

GCSE candidates will find the melodies good dictation practice.

2

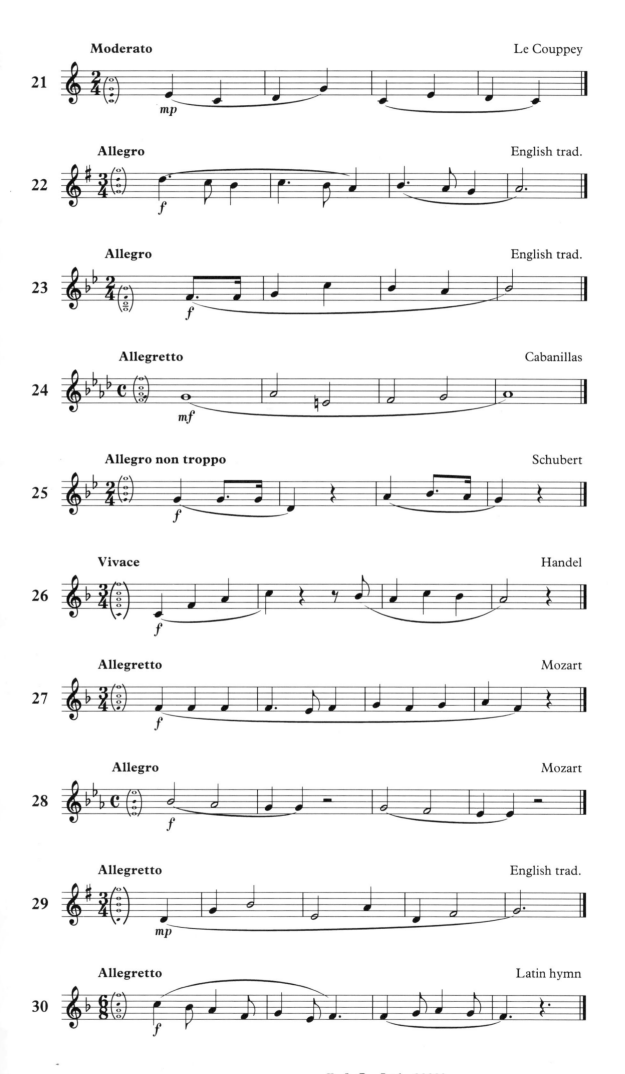

Test B. Sight-Singing in Free Time

These excercises are to be sung at sight in free time. The keychord and the keynote will be given. Any wrong notes will be corrected at the keyboard.

In examinations they are sung to vowels or 'lah', but they also make excellent practice for general aural development for GCSE and other work if they are sung to their letter names or sol-fa names.

Tests are written in treble and bass clefs, and pupils may choose which clef they wish to use in an examination. When practising, however, pupils can also be encouraged to sing from *both* clefs, transposing the starting note down or up an octave as necessary, so that note reading becomes equally fluent in treble and the bass clefs. As well as practising these tests with their teacher, pupils can also be encouraged to practise them on their own, giving themselves keychords and checking their notes with their instrument.

Pupils may have had little previous experience of sight singing, so Exercises 1-36 are very simple. Exercises 37-70 are similar to those which may be found in examinations.

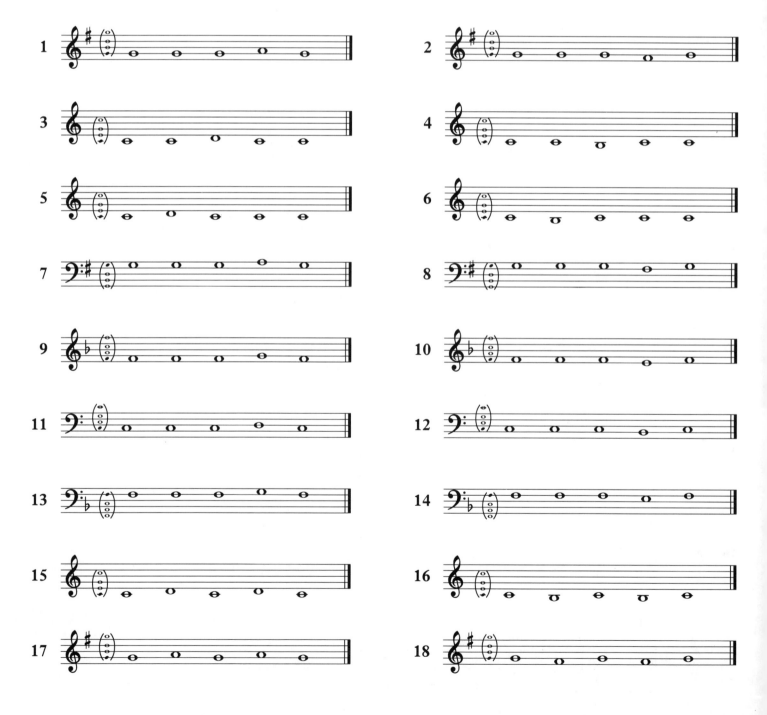

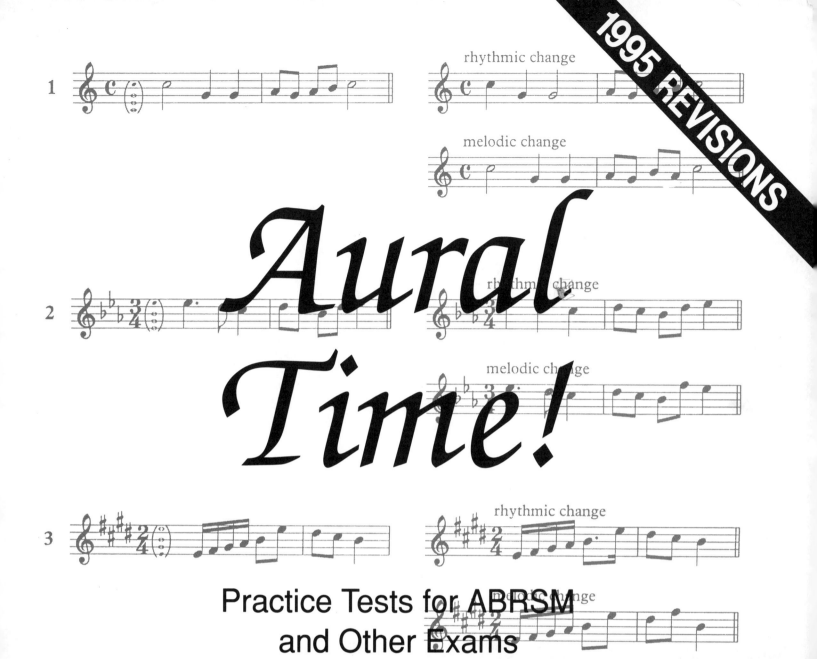

Aural Time!

Practice Tests for ABRSM and Other Exams

Pupil's Book
Grade 4 and Grade 5

DAVID TURNBULL

BOSWORTH

AURAL TIME! Grades 4 and 5.

Pupil's Booklet

In this booklet you will find the sight-singing tests from the 1995 revised editions of *Aural Time!* Grades 4 and 5, and also some hints about musical features, and the way in which they show the historical style and period of a piece.

You can practise the sight-singing exercises by yourself, as well as in lessons with your teacher. Give yourself the keychord and starting note of the test, and check the notes you sing on your instrument. Correct any mistakes you make. You can sing the notes to vowel sounds or to 'lah', but it is also a good idea when practising to sing them to their letter names, or to their sol-fa names, if you know them. You will find that practising these tests will be invaluable, not only for aural tests like those of the Associated Board, but also as general training for the listening papers in GCSE and A level music examinations.

David Turnbull

Grade 4
Sight-Singing Tests in Free Time

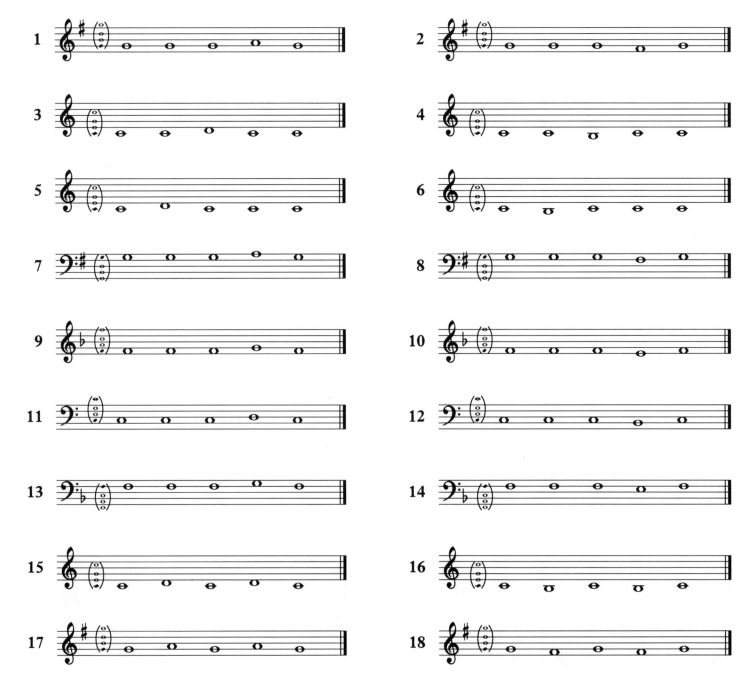

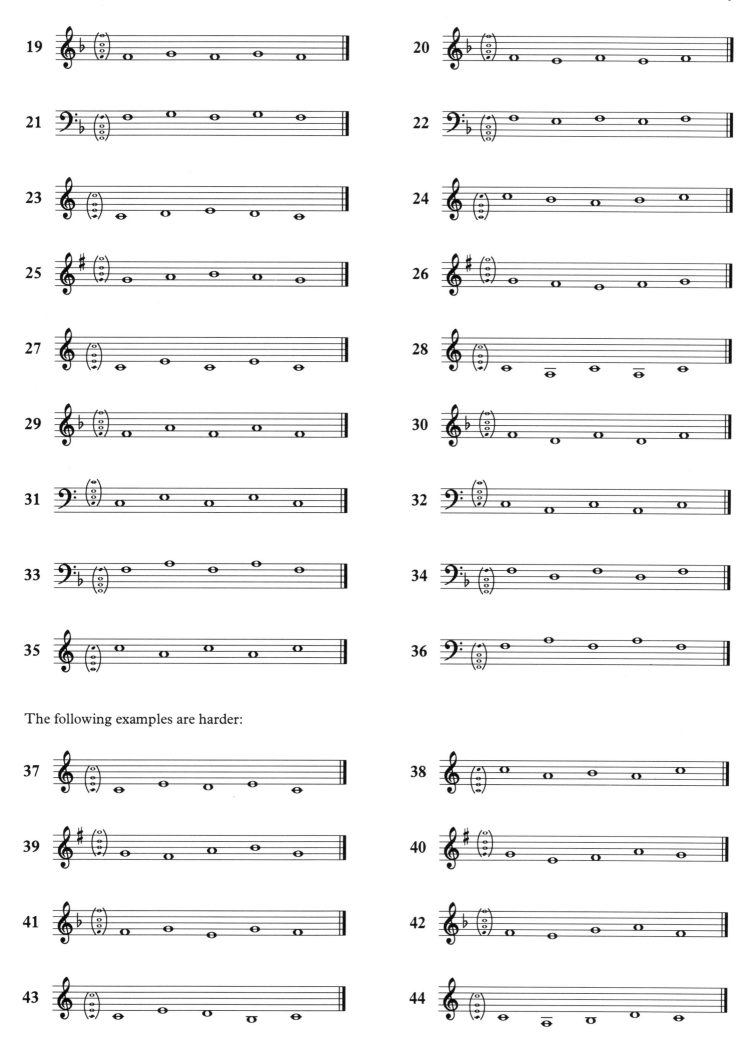

The following examples are harder:

4

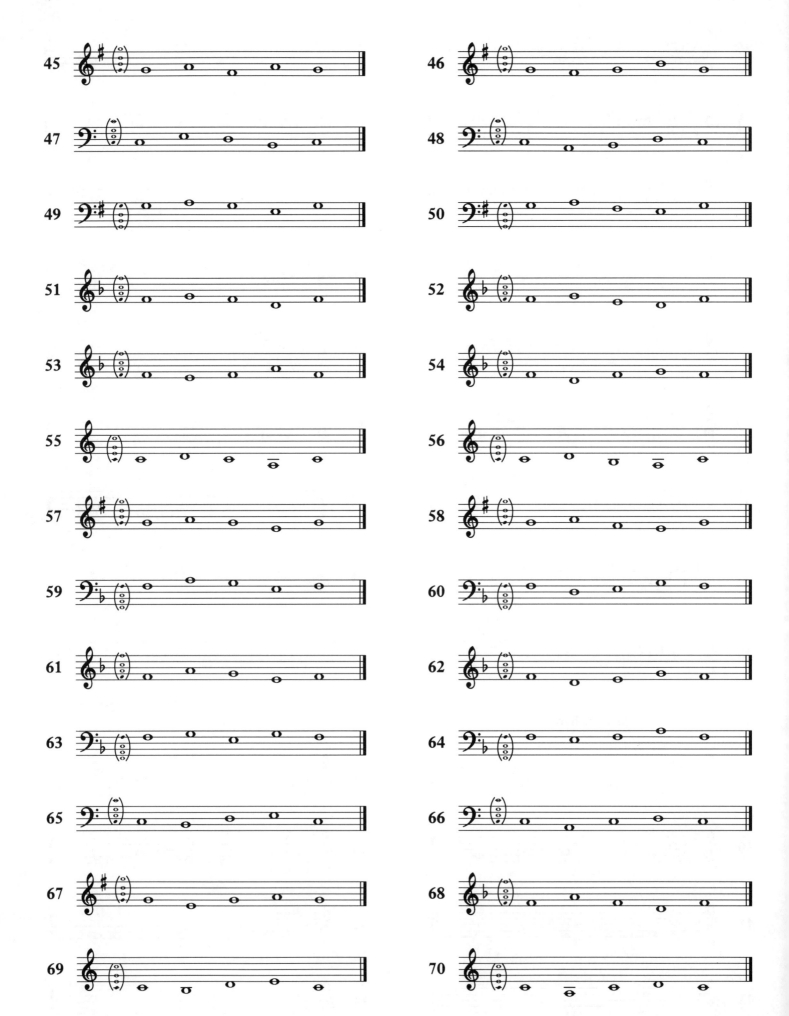

Grade 5
Sight-Singing Tests in Free Time

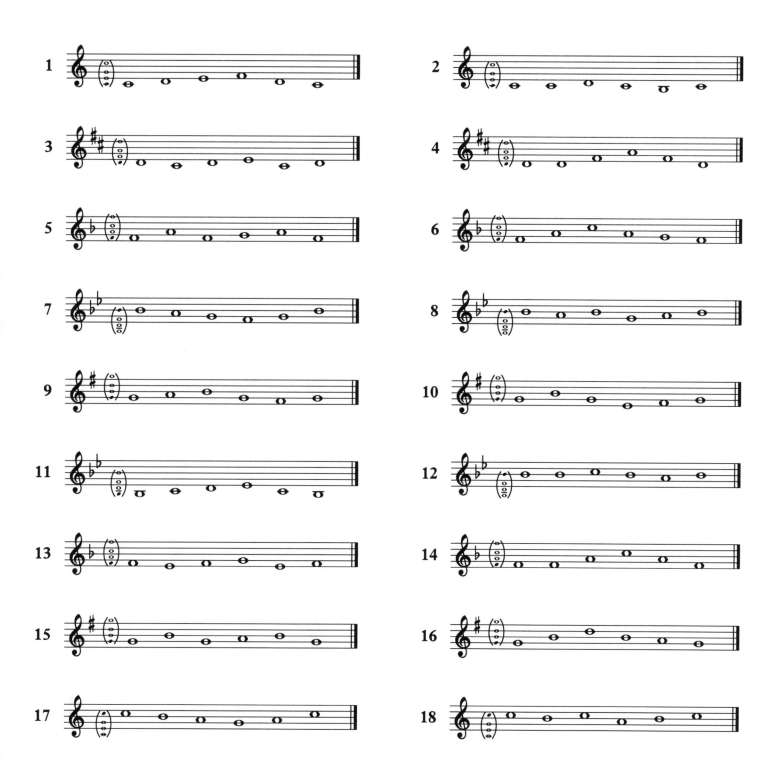

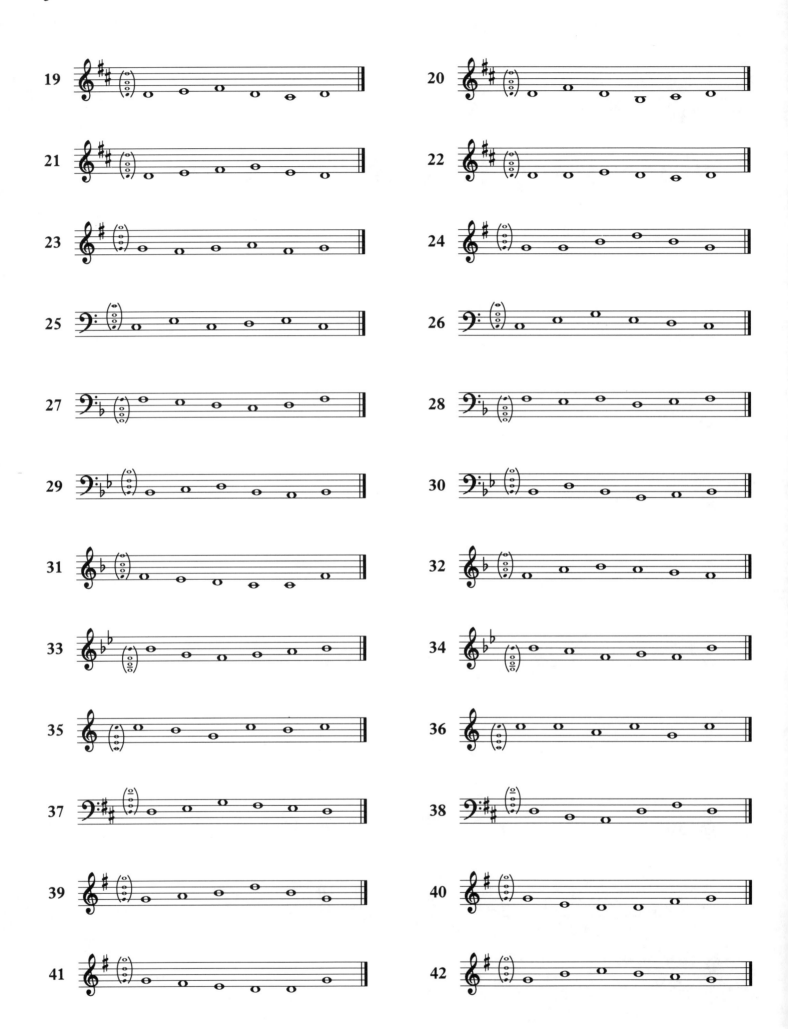

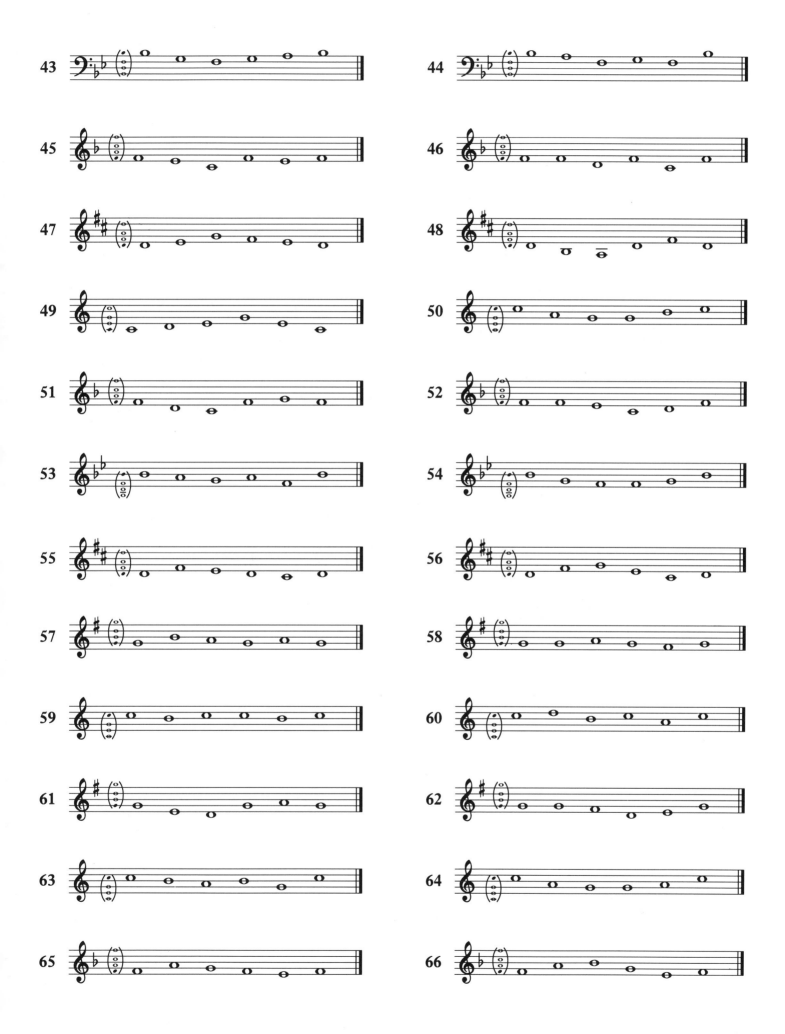

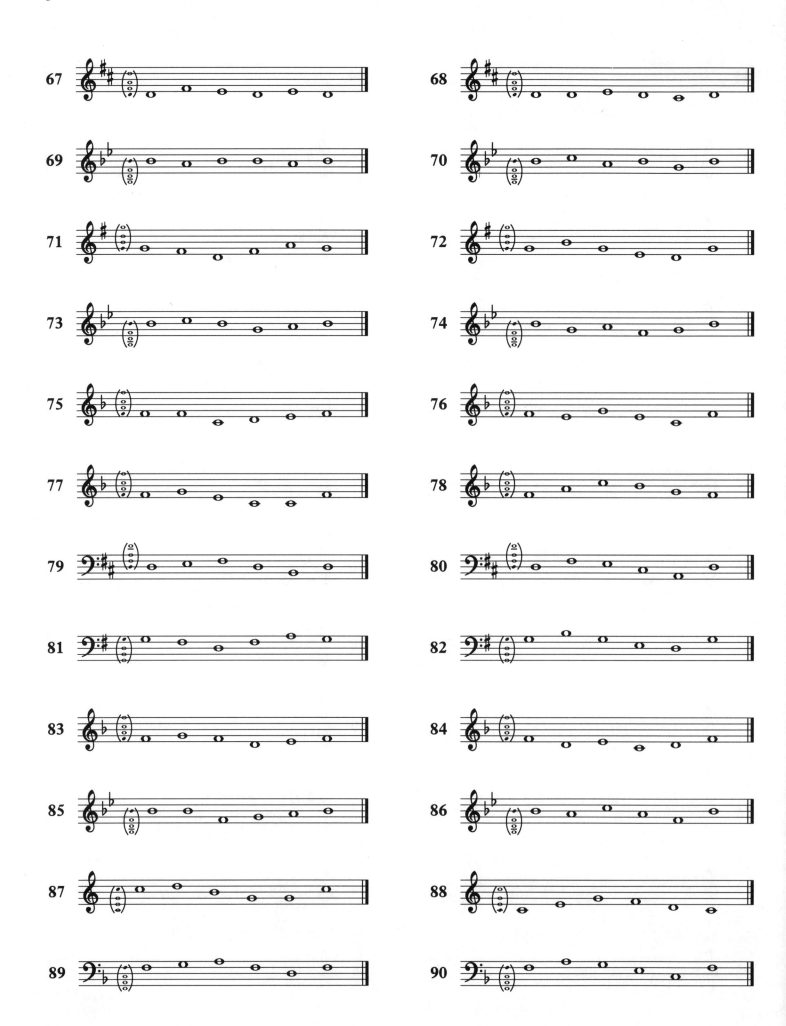

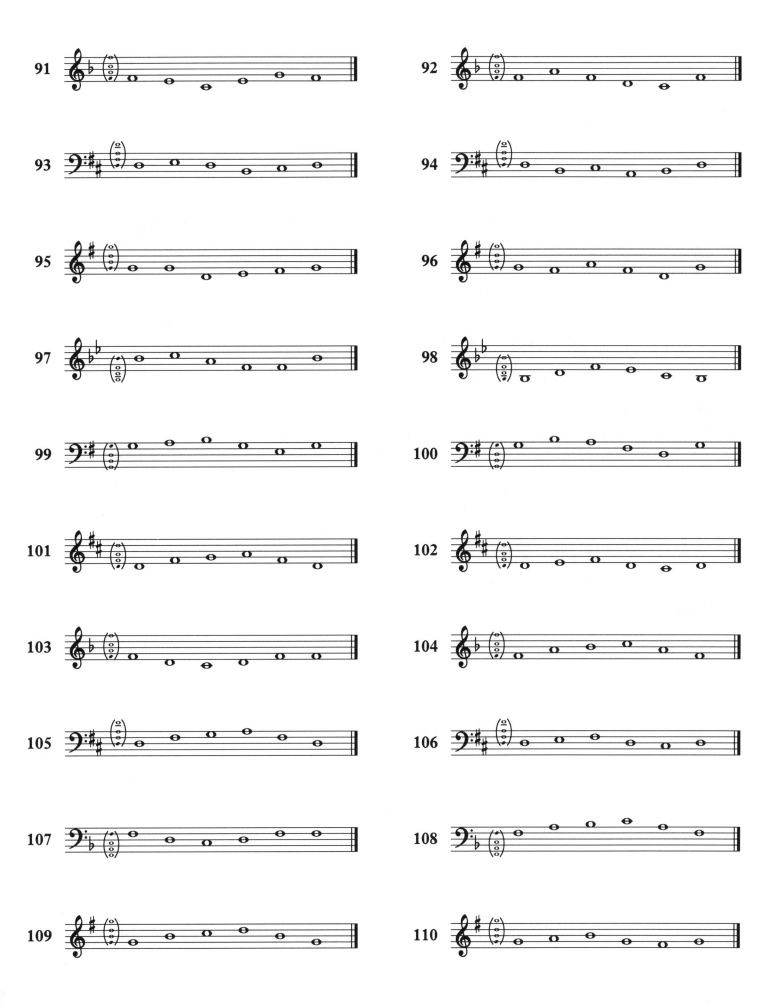

Hints about the musical features of pieces, and historical periods.

Musical Features

In many types of music examination, you may be asked about some features of a piece of music played. These include: **rhythm**; **tempo** (including changes to tempo like *accelerando* and *ritenuto*); **melody**; **form** - the general shape of the music, and whether sections are repeated; **tonality** - the **keys** used, including whether keys are major or minor; **dynamics** - (loud, soft, etc.) and **gradations of dynamics** (like *crescendo* and *diminuendo*); **articulation** of the notes (especially *staccato* and *legato*); **harmony** (the choice and use of chords); **texture**, especially the use of *homophony* (when the piece has a predominant melody which is supported by an accompaniment which is largely chordal), and (b) *counterpoint*, when the piece is constructed in several independent lines - often these lines will imitate each other.

The way the composer uses these features gives to a piece its **character**. For example, if a piece is slow in tempo, is set in a minor key, has articulation which is largely *legato* and has dynamics which are mostly *piano*, the character of the music is likely to be sad. If a piece of music is fast in tempo, in a major key, has articulation which is sometimes *staccato*, and dynamics which are often *forte*, the character of the music is likely to seem bright and cheerful.

Historical periods, and their styles.

An understanding of the features listed above helps to identify the period from which a piece comes. The subject of style is complex and requires experience. Generalisations about styles and periods are difficult because of the many exceptions which occur. However, you should find the following notes useful as a starting point for your studies. Whenever you learn a new piece of music, note its features carefully, and find out in which period the composer worked.

The Baroque period (about 1600-1750).

Baroque composers include J.S. Bach, Handel, D. Scarlatti, Purcell, Corelli and Vivaldi.

Tempo

The tempo of a Baroque movement usually stays the same throughout, with no *accelerandi* or *ritardandi,* apart possibly from a slowing down at the end.

Rhythm

The rhythmic pattern tends to follow the pattern of the beginning of the movement, and phrases are played without too much use of *rubato.*

Melody

Phrases of the melody may be spun out over a considerable length. Baroque melodies often have **ornaments** - trills, mordents, etc.

Key

Keys within a movement are usually closely related to each other, and modulations to remote keys are comparatively rare.

Harmony

Much Baroque harmony is based on the triads of the keys of the piece, though dominant sevenths and more complex chords are often found too. Chromatic notes and suspensions are used sparingly by many Baroque composers.

Texture

Baroque pieces may be homophonic or contrapuntal. In contrapuntal pieces or passages, imitation between parts is often found.

Dynamics

Dynamics are usually 'terraced' - in other words, whole sections of Baroque pieces will be either *piano* or *forte*. *Crescendi* and *diminuendi* are rare, in keyboard music at least, as originally written. Be aware, though, that modern editions sometimes contain dynamic markings which are not in the original style of the composer.

Articulation

Staccato and *legato* notes are found. Much keyboard music of the period was written to be performed on the harpsichord, and when played on a modern piano a *mezzo-staccato* touch is sometimes used.

The **character** and **mood** of a piece are usually the same throughout a Baroque movement.

Forms

of the period include suites of dances like bourrées, gigues, sarabandes and minuets, sonatas (not the same in form as sonatas of the classical period), preludes and fugues, and short pieces, like inventions. Marches are common, in this and all other periods.

The Classical period (about 1750-1820).

Composers of Classical music include Haydn and Mozart.   Some of Beethoven's work is Classical.

Tempo

The tempo of a movement usually remains unchanged throughout, without *accelerandi* or *ritardandi*, and is usually played with little use of *rubato*.

Melody

Phrases are often fairly short, and are often divided into sub-phrases. Phrases tend to have a sense of balance and proportion. Melodies are often ornamented with trills, mordents, etc., but less often than in Baroque music.

Keys within a movement are usually closely related to each other.

Harmony

Mostly based on triads of the keys of the piece, though more complex chords are often met. Chromatic notes and suspensions are usually employed in a restrained way. The sustaining pedal of the piano is used only sparingly.

Texture

Usually basically homophonic, though there may be passages of contrapuntal writing too.

Dynamics

Often change, though rarely very violently.- *Crescendi* and *diminuendi* often found.

Articulation *Staccato* and *legato* frequently used, and also the *tenuto*.

The general **character** and **mood** of a piece is usually the same throughout a movement.

Form

The commonest form of the period is the sonata, often with a minuet as one of the movements.

The Romantic period (about 1820-1900).

Romantic composers include Schumann, Mendelssohn, Chopin, Liszt, Brahms, Dvorák and Tchaikovsky. Some of Schubert's and Beethoven's later work is more Romantic than Classical.

Tempo

The pulse of the tempo of a movement may change frequently, with *accelerandi* and *ritardandi*. Pieces are often performed with considerable use of *rubato*.

Melodies

Often fairly long and highly expressive in character. Ornaments are used, though not as often as in Baroque and Classical music.

Key

Within a movement, key may change frequently. Rich, complicated harmony is often found, which may make much use of complex chords. In piano music, the sustaining pedal is used to emphasise harmony.

Texture

More often basically **homophonic** rather than contrapuntal.

Dynamics

Change often, and often very greatly. *Crescendi* and *diminuendi* are much used.

Articulation

Staccato and *legato* often used, and also the *fermata* (pause).

The general **character** and **mood** may change often during the course of a movement.

Forms of the period include the *sonata*, and also short descriptive pieces. Waltzes are common.

The Modern period (from about 1900 onwards).

Rhythms

Unusual rhythms are often found, with syncopation common. The pulse of the **tempo** of a movement may change frequently.

Melodies may have a jagged shape, and include a wide range of notes.

Key within a movement may change frequently and unexpectedly, and unusual types of scale are often employed.

Harmony is often complex and sometimes very dissonant. The sustaining pedal of the piano is used for harmonic purposes, and the left pedal used to get more contrast in timbre.

Texture may be homophonic or contrapuntal.   **Dynamics** change frequently, and often greatly.

Articulation. *Staccato* and *legato* articulation is widely used, and also the *tenuto*.

Forms are very varied, including most of those met in earlier periods. Some modern forms are not easy to define. Jazz and Blues have forms of their own.

The general **character** and **mood** may change often during the course of a movement, and even from bar to bar.

Printed and bound in Great Britain by Caligraving Limited

BOSWORTH

8/9 Frith Street, London, W1D 3JB
Bosworth GmbH Musikverlag, Friedrichstraβe 153a, 10117 Berlin, Germany

Exclusive distributors:
Music Sales Limited, Newmarket Road, Bury St Edmunds, Suffolk, IP33 3YB

ISBN 1-84449-654-6

Order No: BOE004909

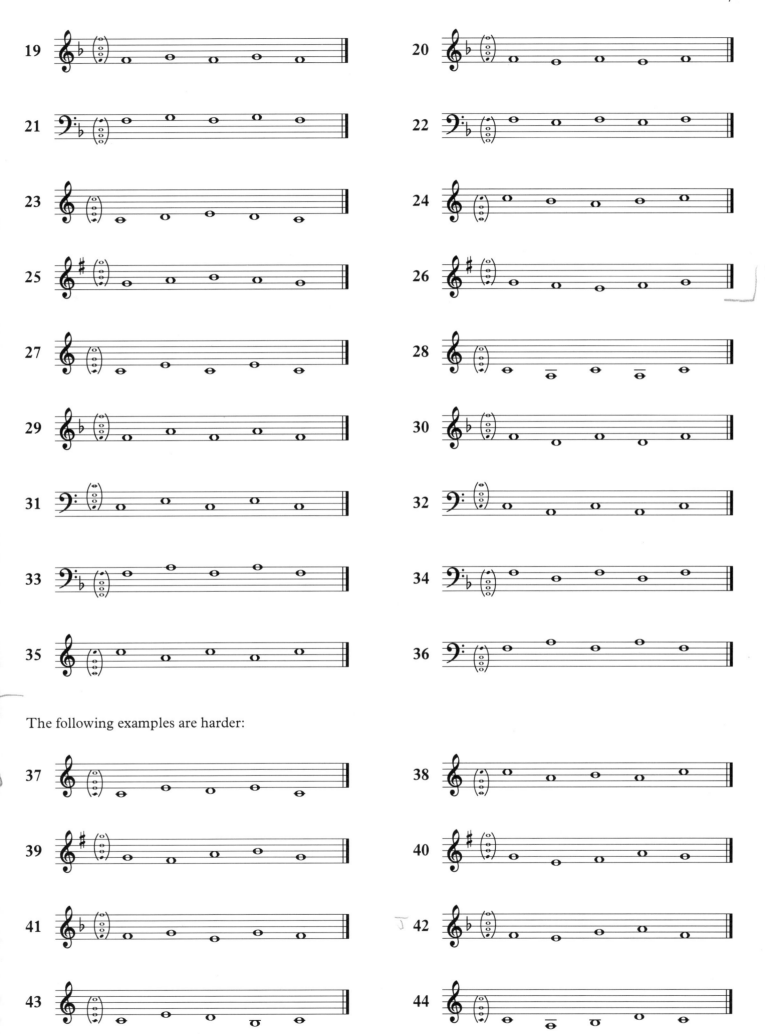

The following examples are harder:

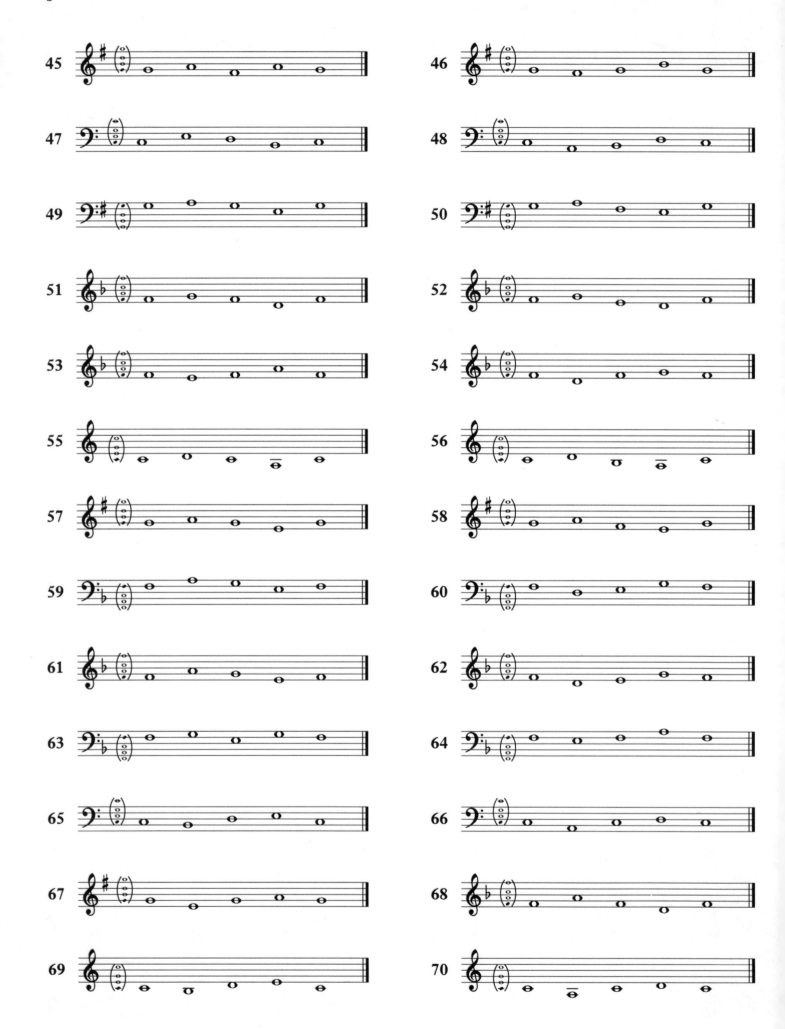

Test C1. Recognising Features.

To the pupil.

You will be asked to comment about some of the following features of pieces in this section:
dynamics (*p/f*), and **gradation of dynamics** (*crescendo/diminuendo*),
articulation of notes (*legato/staccato*);
tempo including changes to tempo (*rallentando,accelerando* etc.);
the recognition of whether the **tonality** (key) is major or minor;
the **character** of the music played.

You will be told which features you will be questioned on before the piece is played.

Test C2. Clapping rhythms

Your teacher will play twice a short extract from the piece used in C1. You must clap back its rhythm, and say if it is in two, three of four time.

To the teacher. For the C2 clapping, two phrases are printed from which you can choose **one**.

C1 *Questions*
      a. Is the **tonality** major or minor?
      b. Describe the **character** of the piece.
      c. Does the **tempo** alter, or stay the same?
      d. Do the **dynamics** alter during the piece? If so, where?

C2 Clap this extract, which will be played twice. After you have clapped it, say if it is in two time, three time or four time.

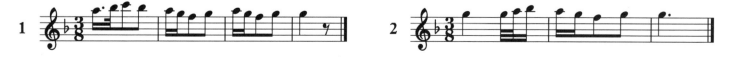

Tempo di Marcia

Mozart: From *"Marriage of Figaro"*

C1 *Questions*
    a. Is the **tonality** major or minor?
    b. Describe the **character** of the piece. Is it like a march, or a dance? Bright, or sad?
    c. Does the **tempo** alter, or stay the same?
    d. Do the **dynamics** alter during the piece? If so, where?

C2 Clap this extract, which will be played twice. After you have clapped it, say if it is in two time, three time or four time.

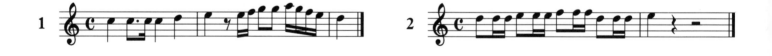

Allegro

Purcell

C1 *Questions*

    a. Is the **tonality** major or minor?

    b. Describe the **character** of the piece.

    c. Does the **tempo** alter, or stay the same?

    d. Do the **dynamics** alter during the piece? If so, where?

    e. Comment on the **articulation** (*legato/staccato*).

C2 Clap this extract, which will be played twice. After you have clapped it, say if it is in two time, three time or four time.

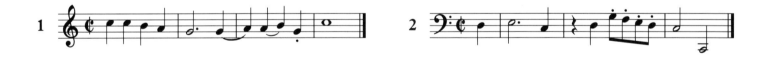

B. & Co. Ltd., 22289

Delibes arr. Heumann

C1 *Questions*

  a. Is the **tonality** major or minor?
  b. Describe the **character** of the piece.
  c. Does the **tempo** alter, or stay the same?
  d. Do the **dynamics** alter during the piece? If so, where?
  e. Is the **articulation** *staccato* or *legato*?

C2 Clap this extract, which will be played twice. After you have clapped it, say if it is in two time, three time or four time.

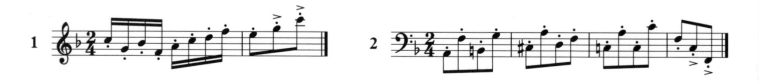

B. & Co. Ltd., 22289

Clementi

C1 *Questions*

    a. Is the **tonality** major or minor?
    b. Describe the **character** of the piece.
    c. Does the **tempo** alter, or stay the same?
    d. Describe the **dynamics** of the piece.
    e. Is the **articulation** at the end *legato* or *staccato*. How does it start?

C2 Clap this extract, which will be played twice. After you have clapped it, say if it is in two time, three time or four time.

B. & Co. Ltd., 22289

C1 *Questions*

    a. Is the **tonality** mostly major or minor?

    b. Describe the **character** of the piece.

    c. Does the **tempo** alter, or stay the same?

    d. Describe the **dynamics**. Does it start softly or loudly? How does it continue?

C2 Clap this extract, which will be played twice. After you have clapped it, say if it is in two time, three time or four time.

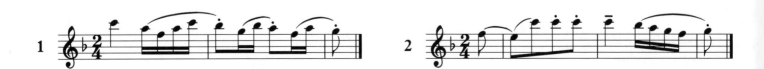

C1 *Questions*
    a. Is the **tonality** mostly major or minor?
    b. Describe the **character** and mood of the piece.
    c. Does the **tempo** alter, or stay the same? If it changes, where does this happen?
    d. Describe the **dynamics**.
    e. Is the **articulation** *legato* or *staccato*.

C2 Clap this extract, which will be played twice. After you have clapped it, say if it is in two time, three time
or four time.

Andante

Kirchner

8

p cantabile

f accel.

dim.

a tempo

p

rall.

C1 *Questions*

    a. Is the **tonality** of this major or minor?

    b. Describe the **character** and mood of the piece.

    c. Does the **tempo** alter. If so, how and where?

    d. Describe the **dynamics**.

    e. Is the **articulation** *legato* or *staccato*.

C2 Clap this extract, which will be played twice. After you have clapped it, say if it is in two time, three time or four time.

1

2

Beethoven

C1 *Questions*

    a. Is the **tonality** at the beginning of this major or minor? Does it change? If so, where?

    b. Does the **character** of the piece stay the same, or does the mood change?

    c. Does the **tempo** alter. If so, how and where?

    d. Describe the **dynamics**.

    e. Is the **articulation** *legato* or *staccato*. Does it alter?

C2 Clap this extract, which will be played twice. After you have clapped it, say if it is in two time, three time or four time.

Wagner: Ride of the Valkyries

Allegro

10

ff

senza rall.

C1 *Questions*

    a. Is the **tonality** at the start major, or minor?

       Are there any alterations in the middle of the piece?

    b. How would you describe the **character** and mood of the music.

    c. Does the **tempo** alter. If so, how and where?

    d. Do the **dynamics** change? If so, where?

C2 Clap this extract, which will be played twice. After you have clapped it, say if it is in two time, three time or four time.

1

2

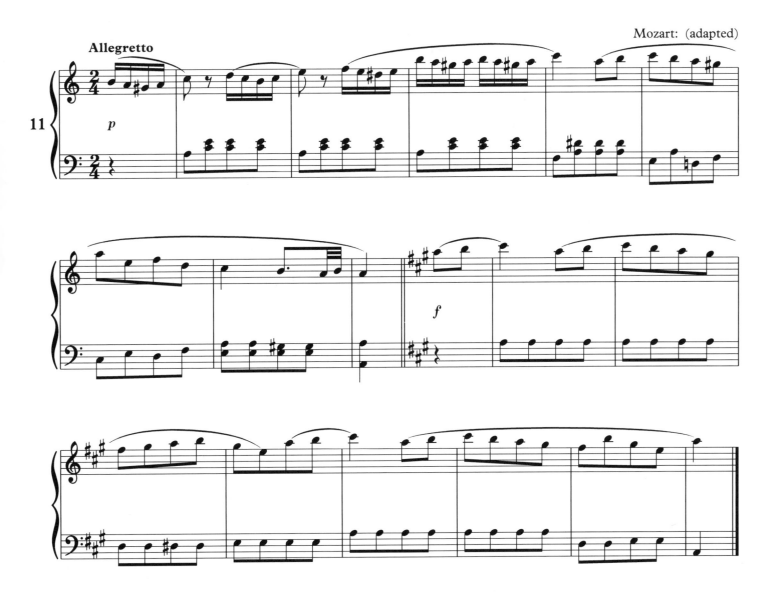

C1 *Questions*
   a. Is the **tonality** at the start major, or minor?
   b. Does it end in a major or minor **key**?
   c. Describe the **character** of the piece.
   d. Describe the **dynamics** used.
   e. Does the **tempo** of the piece change? If so, how?

C2 Clap this extract, which will be played twice. After you have clapped it, say if it is in two time, three time or four time.

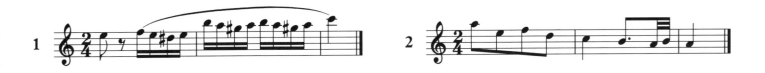

C1 *Questions*

> a. Is the **tonality** major or minor?
> b. How would you describe the **character** and mood of the music?
> c. Does the **tempo** alter. If so, how and where?
> d. Do the **dynamics** change? If so, where?

C2 Clap this extract, which will be played twice. After you have clapped it, say if it is in two time, three time or four time.

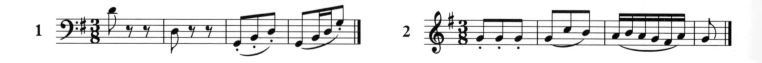

C1 *Questions*

    a. Are the **dynamics** at the end loud or soft?

    b. Is the **tonality** mainly major, or minor?

    c. Does the **key** change ever? If so, where?

    d. Is the **tempo** held steady, or does it change?

    e. Describe the **character** and mood of the music.

C2 Clap this extract, which will be played twice. After you have clapped it, say if it is in two time, three time or four time.

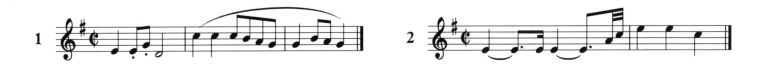

C1 *Questions*
   a. Is the **tonality** mostly major or minor?
   b. Is the **articulation** at the beginning *legato* or *staccato*?
   c. Are there any changes in **tempo**? If so, where?
   d. Discuss the **dynamics** of the last four-bar phrase?

C2 Clap this extract, which will be played twice. After you have clapped it, say if it is in two time, three time or four time.

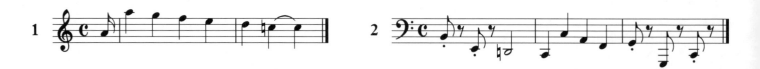

C1 *Questions*

    a. Is the **articulation** at the start *legato* or *staccato*?

    b. Is the **tonality** major, or minor?

    c. Describe the **character** and mood of the music.

    d. Is there any change in **tempo**?

    e. Describe any changes in **dynamics**.

C2 Clap this extract, which will be played twice. After you have clapped it, say if it is in two time, three time or four time.

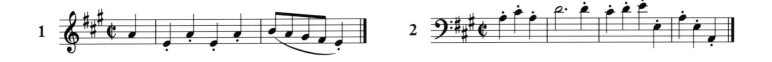

C1 *Questions*
    a. Describe the **dynamics** of the music.
    b. Are there any changes in **tempo**? If so, where do they occur?
    c. Is the **tonality** major, or minor?
    d. Is the **articulation** of the first notes of the melody *legato* or *staccato*?
    e. Describe the **character** and mood of the music.

C2 Clap this extract, which will be played twice. After you have clapped it, say if it is in two time, three time or four time.

Andante

Enckhausen (adapted)

17

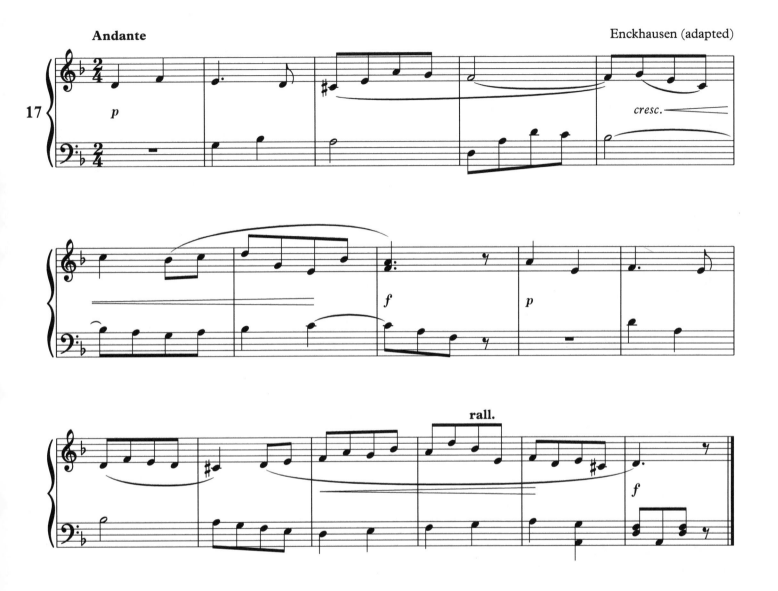

C1 *Questions*
    a. Does the music start in a major or a minor **key**?
    b. Does the **tonality** change at all? If so, where?
    c. Are there any modifications to the **tempo**? If so, where?
    d. Describe any changes in **dynamics**.
    e. Is the **articulation** of this piece mostly *legato* or *staccato*?

C2 Clap this extract, which will be played twice. After you have clapped it, say if it is in two time, three time or four time.

Allegro tranquillo

Schütt (adapted)

18

p dolce espress.

mf più express.

tranquillo

molto rit.

accel.

C1 *Questions*

a. Describe any changes of **tempo**.

b. Comment on the **character** and mood of the music.

c. Describe the **dynamics** used in the music.

d. Is the **tonality** at the start major, or minor?

e. Is the music mostly *staccato* or *legato* in its **articulation**?

C2 Clap this extract, which will be played twice. After you have clapped it, say if it is in two time, three time or four time.

Vivace

Liszt: *Hungarian Rhapsody* (adapted)

poco a poco accelerando

a tempo

poco a poco accelerando

C1 *Questions*

    a. Is the **tonality** major, or minor?

    b. Describe any changes in **tempo**.

    c. Is the **articulation** of the first note of the melody *staccato* or *legato*?

    d. Describe the **character** and style of the music.

    e. Does the first strong accent fall on the first note? If not, on which note does it fall?

C2 Clap this extract, which will be played twice. After you have clapped it, say if it is in two time, three time or four time.

Moderato risoluto

Bach

20

C1 *Questions*

    a. Describe the **character** and mood of this music.
    b. Are there any changes in **tempo**?
    c. Is the **tonality** major, or minor?
    d. Is the **articulation** just before the end *legato* or *staccato*?

C2 Clap this extract, which will be played twice. After you have clapped it, say if it is in two time, three time or four time.

1

2

Printed and bound in Great Britain by
Caligraving Limited Thetford Norfolk

B. & Co. Ltd., 22289

5/05 (55094)